Pilot Ollie &
Pilot Polly's
Amazing Adventure

www. planecharacters.com

Plane Characters Ltd©

Flag Hunt!
See if you can
find all the
Italian flags.

1

"Good morning Megan, good morning Molly, good morning Mike," Pilot Ollie greets the flight attendants as he arrives at work.

Flight attendants are also known as cabin crew. Before every flight, they have a meeting to discuss the in-flight service.

They are getting ready for today's flight when Pilot Ollie arrives.

In the briefing room, Pilot Ollie finds a large folder packed full of maps and charts that Chris Controller has left there for him.

Pilot Ollie sits down and opens the folder. On top is a large map that shows the whole of Europe.

Chris Controller has drawn a line on the map with a red pen showing Pilot Ollie his route for today. Can you guess where he is going?

Today Pilot Ollie is flying to Rome, the capital of Italy.

"Yippee!" he says. "I love Rome, especially the sights and the food."

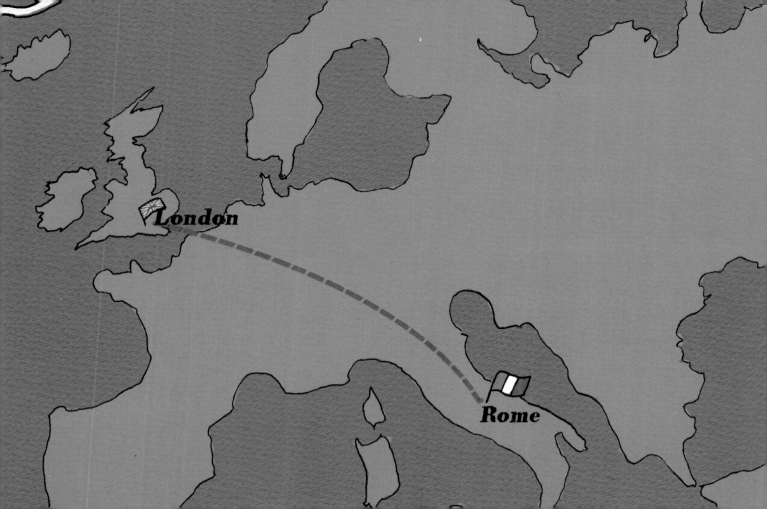

Pilot Ollie puts the flight folder in his case, walks out of the briefing room and over to his plane. He climbs up the steps and takes his seat in the flight deck.

Soon the excited passengers join him and take their seats in the cabin.

The plane has been checked by Alfie Engineer overnight and is now looking shiny and new in the bright sunlight.

"ROOOOAAARRR" go the engines as Pilot Ollie presses the button that starts the big jets. The steps are pulled away by the ground crew.

"**Chocks Away**," calls Pilot Ollie "We're ready to go!"

Pilot Ollie puts on his seatbelt and his headset so that he can talk to Chris Controller on the radio.

"This is Pilot Ollie requesting permission to takeoff to Rome," he says into the microphone.

"You are cleared for takeoff," replies Chris from the control tower. "Have a nice flight."

Pilot Ollie increases the power on the big jet engines.

The plane's engines get louder and louder as it races down the runway getting faster and faster. Then it lifts off into the sky.

Pilot Ollie and his passengers are on their way to Rome.

During the flight Pilot Ollie uses the plane's computers to help him find his way to Rome.

In the flight deck there are lots of computer screens, one of them showing a map of where the plane is flying over.

On the map, Pilot Ollie can also see where the mountains are and the big rain clouds.

Flying through big rain clouds makes the flight bumpy so Pilot Ollie steers the plane around them.

Woody Weatherman left Pilot Ollie some weather charts in the flight folder.

Can you see from the picture what the weather is like?

It's warm and sunny when they arrive in Rome two hours later. Pilot Ollie says goodbye to all of the passengers as they get off the plane.

Then it's time to go and explore.

None of the cabin crew have ever been to Rome, so Pilot Ollie offers to show them around.

"Follow me," he says as they head into town. "First of all, let's do some sightseeing."

There are many amazing things to see in Rome. Pilot Ollie decides to take the crew to his favourite place.

"This is the Colosseum," he says when they arrive at a huge, round building.

"What is it?" asks Flight Attendant Mike as he snaps a picture with his camera.

"The Colosseum is an 'amphitheatre'," explains Pilot Ollie. "That means it's an outdoor theatre. It was built by the ancient Romans nearly 2,000 years ago and is the largest amphitheatre in the world".

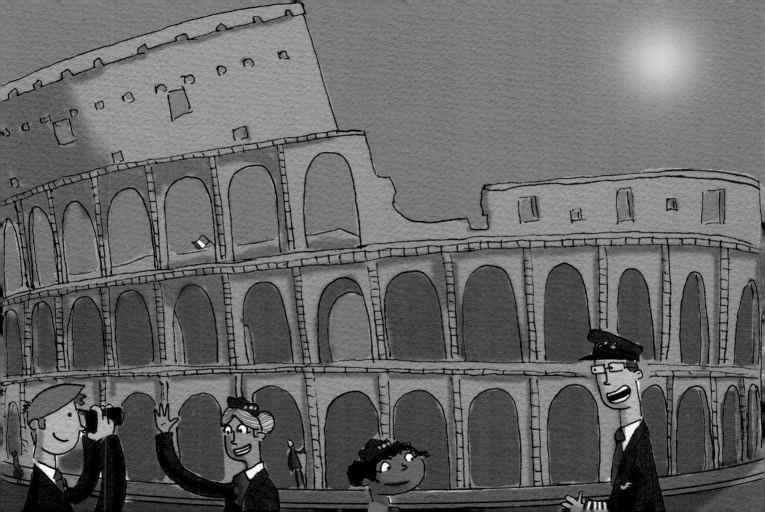

"It's so big and so old!" exclaims Flight Attendant Megan. "But I've heard that Rome is very good for shopping too. Can we go shopping now?"

Megan is right. Rome is famous for its shopping, so the crew set off to look around the shops.

A few days ago, Pilot Ollie noticed that his left foot had got wet in a puddle. "There must be a hole in these old shoes," he thought. "I need to buy new ones."

Rome is known for making great shoes, so Pilot Ollie sets off to find a new pair. As he wanders down some narrow streets, Pilot Ollie suddenly spots the shiniest pair of shoes he has ever seen in a little shop window.

The shoes are so shiny that the sunlight bounces off them and dazzles him.

He goes into the little shop and tries on the shiny shoes, which fit perfectly. Pilot Ollie pays for them, asks the shop keeper to throw away his old, broken shoes and excitedly walks out of the shop with his new shoes.

Outside, the crew are waiting. Pilot Ollie can hear their tummies grumbling loudly. "We are so hungry!" says Flight Attendant Mike.

"Then let's go get some lunch," replies Pilot Ollie. "Anyone else fancy a pizza?" asks Flight Attendant Megan, and the rest of the crew nod their heads in agreement.

Roman pizza is unique, it is very, very thin. The crew continue walking until they find a little Pizzeria where they sit down around a table outside in the sunshine.

The crew look at the menu and choose their favourite pizzas.

What pizza would you choose?

When the pizzas arrive, they are so huge that they don't even fit on the plates!

But after all the sightseeing and shopping the crew are so hungry that they quickly eat up everything.

"I love it in Rome," says Molly. "I hope I can come back again soon".

Pilot Ollie has an idea. Once again he says "Follow me," to the crew and starts walking.

Pilot Ollie takes them down some narrow streets which lead to a beautiful fountain.

"This is the Trevi Fountain," says Pilot Ollie "and legend has it that if you throw a coin over your shoulder into the fountain, you will one day come back to Rome."

The crew all stand together with their backs to the fountain and throw their coins over their shoulders.

"The fountains are beautiful," says Megan. "I'm definitely coming back here!"

Then it is time to head back to the airport for the flight home, but Pilot Ollie has a surprise in store for the crew before they leave.

As they walk back, he buys them all a treat. Italy is famous for its ice cream, called gelato. Megan tries chocolate, Mike has strawberry, Molly vanilla and Pilot Ollie lemon.

What is your favourite Gelato Flavour?

Back on the plane, the crew once again go through all of their pre-flight checks. Pilot Ollie looks around the plane's wheels and engines making sure they are safe for the flight.

When the crew are ready the passengers board the plane and they are ready to go. Molly closes the big plane door.

"**Chocks Away!**" calls Pilot Ollie. He starts the big jet engines and taxies to the runway.

The controllers in Rome talk to Pilot Ollie on the radio and clear him to takeoff.

"Thank you Rome," says Pilot Ollie "We've had a lovely day. See you soon."

The engines **ROOOAAARRR** and the plane takes off. The passengers and the crew are on their way home.